THREE MODERATELY CAUTIONARY TALES

———————— or ————————

Fifty Etchings on Relief

Alexander Massouras

Three Moderately Cautionary Tales

1

THE GILDERBOOK

Paul was a gilder.

Fig. 1

He loved the glint of gold.

Fig. 2

One day, Paul gilded all the picture frames in his house.

Fig. 3

It wasn't quite right, so he gilded the walls too.

Fig. 4

In the kitchen he mused: something was wrong.

Fig. 5

So he gilded the table;

Fig. 6

the chairs;

Fig. 7

and then his parakeets, Myrtle and Mae.

Fig. 8

Upstairs (and those were gilded too),

Fig. 9

with much deftness, Paul gilded his bed to better dream of gold.

Fig. 10

The time came when Paul's entire house was golden
and shone like the sun.

Fig. 11

And then the doorbell rang.

Fig. 12

Friends were calling, and Paul felt immediately happy.

Fig. 13

Together they set off.

Fig. 14

And Paul soon forgot his golden house.

Fig. 15

2

HIERONYMUS
THE LION TAMER

PART ONE: THE DIFFICULTY

Hieronymus was a lion tamer.

Fig. 16

He was known everywhere for his spectacular bravery
and brilliant tricks.

Fig. 17

But the fearsomeness with which Hieronymus tamed lions frightened everything else away too.

Fig. 18

So Hieronymus passed the time with his lions.

Fig. 19

And his house, for all its magnificence, felt lonely and cold.

Fig. 20

Noticing the advent of winter one morning,
Hieronymus decided to go shopping for a jumper.

Fig. 21

"Ugh, the cold," he shuddered.
A lion heard and stayed within.

Fig. 22

He found a jumper, but when lifted from the rail it fell limp with fear. "I shall have it nevertheless," roared Hieronymus, hiding his dismay.

Fig. 23

The shopkeeper, terrified by Hieronymus,
cowered and then fled.

Fig. 24

Hieronymus sought comfort by feeding the ducks.
But they would only jump on cones

Fig. 25

or hold their beaks open
(as if waiting for Hieronymus to place his head there).

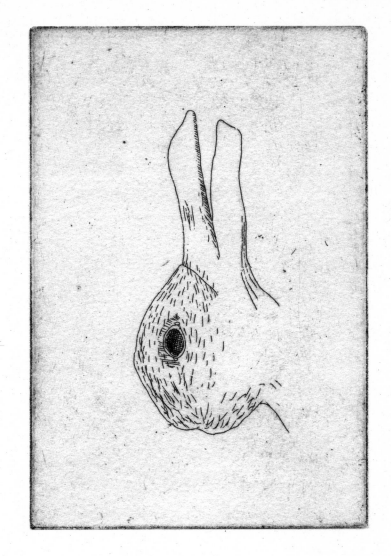

Fig. 26

Hieronymus trudged home. It was raining, but the drops did not dare to land on him.

Fig. 27

He arrived quite dry. "I have of late grown tired of taming,"
Hieronymus bellowed over a trembling tea.
He wondered whether there might be a cure.

Fig. 28

The following day, he visited his doctor,
who with grim inevitability leapt through hoops of fire.
Since he offered no cure, Hieronymus left.

Fig. 29

As Hieronymus emerged, a bee landed on his hand.
"A brave bee," he thought, noticing first its absence of acrobatics,
and then a humming sound which grew gradually louder.

Fig. 30

Ambrose the beekeeper was near.

Fig. 31

Hieronymus returned the bee. As he did so, Ambrose related his own affliction:

Fig. 32

So calming was his company
that once, while summoning the fire brigade,
Ambrose was met with snoring.

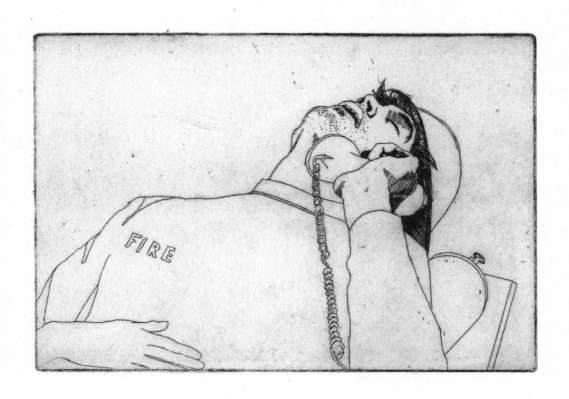

Fig. 33

If he tried to take a peaceful amble in the park,
dogs would swarm around him.

Fig. 34

(And sometimes so would people.)

Fig. 35

PART THREE: AN EPIPHANY

Thus Hieronymus had an epiphany.

Fig. 36

They would trade places. Ambrose handed over his bees and Hieronymus relinquished the keys to his lion house.

Fig. 37

Hieronymus was a beekeeper.

Fig. 38

Ambrose was a lion tamer.

Fig. 39

3

ALFRED'S LIBRARY

From the very beginning, Alfred pursued knowledge.

Fig. 40

Sometimes through discourse,

Fig. 41

most often from books.

Fig. 42

Often, too often.

Fig. 43

Book by book, he accumulated a stupendous library,

Fig. 44

which grew to unimaginable heights.

Fig. 45

And Alfred found himself on a tower of knowledge, knowing.

Fig. 46

Retrieving a botanical book from the base one day,
Alfred caused an accident. The tower fell.

Fig. 47

Alfred's words were broken.

Fig. 48

"Boo," thought Alfred in so many words.

Fig. 49

And he decided to rest.

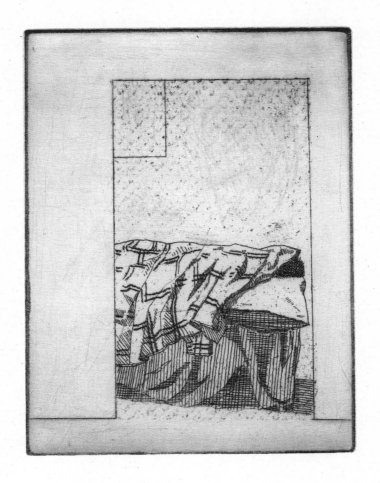

Fig. 50

Images: fifty hard-ground etchings
Image size: 100 x 150 mm
Sheet size: 190 x 275 mm

First published in 2011 by Julian Page
Printed in England by Ex Why Zed on recycled paper
© Alexander Massouras and Julian Page 2011
All rights reserved

A full catalogue record of this book is available from the British Library.
ISBN 978-0-9570124-0-0